THE LION, THE WITCH AND THE WARDROBE

Based upon the story by C. S. Lewis

Dramatized by

Joseph Robinette

Dramatic Publishing

Woodstock, Illinois • England • Australia • New Zealand

THE LION, THE WITCH AND THE WARDROBE

A Full Length Play
For a cast of 16 performers and extras*

CHARACTERS

ASLAN ....a great lion
WHITE WITCH ....an evil queen
LUCY, EDMUND, SUSAN, PETER .... children
MR. & MRS. BEAVER .... forest animals
 UNICORN, CENTAUR .... forest animals
TUMNUS .... a faun
FENRIS ULF .. a wolf, head of the Witch's secret police
DWARF ....a servant to the Witch
FATHER CHRISTMAS ....a bringer of gifts
ELF .... Father Christmas' helper
WHITE STAG ....an elusive omen of good fortune

EXTRAS

ASLAN'S FOLLOWERS .... forest animals
WITCH'S ARMY ....evil villains
WOOD NYMPHS .... stage helpers

PLACE: A mansion and the Land of Narnia.
TIME: The 1940's or the present.

*An optional intermission is designated in the script.
With the exception of the four children, all characters may
be played by males or females.

THE LION, THE WITCH AND THE WARDROBE

PROLOGUE*

SCENE. *In front of the main curtain—or a scrim—four children enter. From oldest to youngest they are: PETER, SUSAN, EDMUND, and LUCY. ALL except EDMUND look about in wide-eyed fascination.*

SUSAN. What an exciting old mansion!

EDMUND. I think it's boring.

SUSAN. Oh, Edmund.

PETER. Come on, Ed. It'll be a fun place to explore.

LUCY. I'm glad Mother and Father let us come out to the country for a few days.

SUSAN. I'm going to love staying here with the old professor. Isn't he a dear?

PETER. Yes. But I'm not sure I like his housekeeper. *(Mimicking the housekeeper.)* "Please remember to always stay out of my way!" *(They laugh. PETER points off, R.)* Hey, let's go look at that room that has all the swords and suits of armor inside.

SUSAN. You go ahead, Peter. I think I'll go back down to the library and look through some books. How about you, Lucy?

LUCY *(pointing off, L).* That room over there seems very interesting.

EDMUND *(crossing a few steps L and looking off).* There's nothing in it but an old clock and a big wardrobe.

LUCY. But it's the largest wardrobe I've ever seen. I want to take a closer look at it. *(She exits off, L.)*

PETER. Come on, Ed.

EDMUND *(unenthused)*. I'd rather explore outside.

PETER. But it's raining. Let's go to the sword room.

EDMUND. All right. But only till we can go outside.

SUSAN. Don't get lost. It's almost time for dinner.

EDMUND. Oh, Susan. Stop talking like Mother. *(He and PETER exit off, R.)*

SUSAN. Well, somebody needs to be in charge since Mother and Father aren't here. *(Looking off, L.)* Lucy! *(Crossing L.)* Come downstairs to the library with me. It'll be a lot more fun than an old room with nothing but a wardrobe in it. *(Peering off.)* Lucy?...I thought she went in there. *(Crossing back C.)* I guess she changed her mind. *(Looking about as she smiles.)* Well...I think our stay here is going to be quite an adventure — quite an adventure indeed. *(She exits off, R. The Prologue ends as the curtain — or scrim — rises to reveal a setting which suggests a wooded area.)*

*The Prologue is optional. The play may begin when the curtain rises on Narnia (p. 7).

SCENE ONE

SCENE: *The stage is basically bare except for a few trees and foliage and a lamppost at R. Several different levels may be used for the play's various locales. A backdrop — or a cut-out silhouette — at the rear suggests distant castles. The simple set changes will be done by three (or more) WOOD NYMPHS during the course of the play. No curtain is necessary between scenes. Simple lighting changes may be used to define the various locales as each is used.*

A cold wind blows as snowflakes fall. A WHITE STAG enters quickly, pauses, sniffs the air, then exits hurriedly. A moment later, a UNICORN enters breathlessly. He searches in vain for the WHITE STAG, then gives up.

UNICORN. I'll never catch him. Never.

(MR. AND MRS. BEAVER enter exhaustedly.)

MRS. BEAVER. Hello, Mr. Unicorn.
UNICORN. Oh, good morning, Mrs. Beaver... Mr. Beaver.
MR. BEAVER. What's so good about it?
MRS. BEAVER *(to UNICORN)*. What are you doing out so early?
UNICORN. I was trying to catch the White Stag. But I missed him again.
MRS. BEAVER. Well, don't give up. The White Stag will bring you good fortune if you catch him.
UNICORN. I know.

MR. BEAVER. It will take more than good fortune to help any of us.

MRS. BEAVER. Poor dear. He's in a bad mood. His dam broke last night.

MR. BEAVER. It's more than that. It's this blasted cold weather. I'll never get used to it.

UNICORN. But it's always cold weather in Narnia, Mr. Beaver. There's nothing to be done about it.

(A CENTAUR enters.)

CENTAUR. Maybe there is something to be done about it.

MRS. BEAVER. And what's that, Mr. Centaur?

CENTAUR. We can hope and pray that our King will soon return.

MRS. BEAVER. We keep hoping and praying, but he has not been seen for years. Not in my time—or even in my father's time.

CENTAUR. Then we must all have more faith.

MRS. BEAVER. I think Mr. Centaur is right.

UNICORN. I think so, too.

MR. BEAVER. I think—we should break up this meeting in a hurry.

CENTAUR. Why is that, Mr. Beaver?

MR. BEAVER. Shh. Listen. *(Off, voices are heard.)*

VOICE OF FENRIS ULF *(off)*. Come on, you! No more stalling.

UNICORN. It sounds like Fenris Ulf.

CENTAUR. Not that scoundrel.

VOICE OF TUMNUS *(off)*. I'm terribly sorry, sir.

UNICORN. And Tumnus, the Faun.

MRS. BEAVER. Poor Tumnus. How did he ever get himself mixed up in that bad business.

MR. BEAVER. Whatever the reason, he's in a mess. And we will be, too, if we're seen by that rascal Fenris Ulf.

UNICORN. Mr. Beaver is right. Goodbye, everybody.

CENTAUR. Goodbye. And don't forget to pray diligently for the return of the King.

(ALL agree and exit quickly just as FENRIS ULF, a wolf in military attire, enters holding TUMNUS, a faun, by the scruff of the neck. ULF looks about suspiciously.)

ULF. Who was just here? What was that flurry of activity?

TUMNUS *(fearfully)*. Probably—just a blizzard, sir.

ULF. Probably the enemy. But they scatter swiftly on the arrival of Fenris Ulf, Captain of the Queen's Secret Police. Now, why were you late coming to your post again this morning?

TUMNUS. But I really don't think I'm needed here, sir. A child of Adam and Eve has never come this way before.

ULF. But one will come someday, and it's your job to trap him. In fact, a child of Adam and Eve may come along even today. *(He sniffs.)* There is the smell of a human in the air. And remember, if he comes and you let him escape, you know what the Queen will do to you.

TUMNUS. Turn me into a stone statue?

ULF. At the very least. Now, I must check on the other sentinels. Maintain your post, knave.

TUMNUS. Yes, sir. Whatever you say, sir. *(ULF exits.)* Oh, how did I ever get myself in this fix? My father would be so disappointed in me. Oh, well, if I'm lucky, maybe a human will *never* come this way. *(A pause.)* But if one does, I can take him to the Queen, and she'll reward me. But that would be wrong—I think. Oh, I'm perplexed—as usual. I don't know what to do —except what I usually do when I'm perplexed. Play my pipe.

(TUMNUS begins to play a tune on a reed pipe. A moment later, LUCY enters at R. She backs into the area looking about as though confused and surprised. She does not see TUMNUS nor does he see her. The two bump into each other. TUMNUS drops his pipe.)

TUMNUS. Goodness gracious me!

LUCY. Oh, I'm terribly sorry. *(She picks up the pipe and gives it to him.)*

TUMNUS. Who are you?

LUCY. My—my name is Lucy.

TUMNUS. Lucy—are you a daughter of Eve?

LUCY. A what?

TUMNUS. A daughter of Eve. A *human.*

LUCY. Of course I'm human.

TUMNUS. Good. Allow me to introduce myself. My name is Tumnus. I'm a faun.

LUCY *(shaking his hand).* I am very pleased to meet you, Mr. Tumnus.

TUMNUS. May I ask, O Lucy, Daughter of Eve, how have you come into Narnia?

LUCY. Narnia? What's that?

TUMNUS. It's this. All the land that lies between this lamppost and the great castle of Cair Paravel on the Eastern Sea is Narnia. How did you get here?

LUCY. It's very hard to explain. You see, I was exploring
with my sister and two brothers—

TUMNUS. Oh, there are four of you. Will the others be
coming as well?

LUCY. I don't know. I'm not even sure how *I* got here.
We were visiting this house in the country, and I
climbed into a large wardrobe in a spare room.

TUMNUS. War Drobe? Spare Oom?

LUCY. Spare *room*. Yes. Then I realized there was no
back to the wardrobe. And suddenly, I was here in—
in—

TUMNUS. Narnia. Oh, you'll be so glad you came. And I
hope the others will find their way here, too, so that I
can show all of you our beautiful country—and introduce you to our lovely witch—uh, *Queen.*

LUCY *(looking around)*. Everything seems so—magical.

TUMNUS. Oh, it is. And you can be anywhere you wish
in Narnia—quick as a wink. For instance you can take
a trip to the distant castle Cair Paravel—*(A light comes
up on the outline of a castle.)* Or the home of the
mighty wi—, uh, *Queen. (Another light silhouettes a second castle.)* Or you may wish to picnic at the great
Stone Table.

*(The WOOD NYMPHS enter and put the Stone Table in
place U.)*

TUMNUS. Or perhaps you would like to visit the home
of two of our forest friends—Mr. and Mrs. Beaver, for
example. *(The WOOD NYMPHS quickly set up a few
chairs and a table at L.)* Or even my own humble
abode. *(The WOOD NYMPHS set up two or three small
furniture pieces at R. On a small table are a teapot and*

two cups.) Tumnus Towers, I call it. I like fancy names for simple things.

LUCY *(in awe)*. It's a fascinating place.

TUMNUS. Perfect for the imagination—with a bit of help from the Wood Nymphs. *(He waves to the WOOD NYMPHS as they exit.)*

LUCY. There's only one small problem here, as I see it.

TUMNUS. Yes?

LUCY. It's so cold. It was summer just a few minutes ago—where I came from, I mean.

TUMNUS. In the land of Spare Oom?

LUCY *(laughing)*. Yes.

TUMNUS. Well, to be truthful, it is always winter in Narnia, but you'll get use to it. I hope. Meanwhile, why don't we repair to Tumnus Towers for a spot of tea to warm us up.

LUCY. Very well. I can see no harm in it.

TUMNUS. None at all. *(He leads her to his "home," and they enter. He pours tea.)* The Wood Nymphs have even brewed tea for us. Here you are. *(He serves her a cup, and she drinks.)*

LUCY. Thank you. It's delicious. *(He begins to play his pipe.)* I'm so glad I met you, Mr. Tumnus. You're a very nice faun. *(A pause as she nods dreamily to the music.)* And your music is lovely. It makes me so warm and sleepy. *(She closes her eyes for a moment. TUMNUS abruptly stops playing his pipe.)*

TUMNUS. No!

LUCY. What—what is it?

TUMNUS. It's not true.

LUCY. What's not true?

TUMNUS. I'm not a nice faun. In fact, I'm a very bad faun. *(He sobs. LUCY hands him her handkerchief.)*

LUCY. Not at all. You're the best faun I ever met.

TUMNUS. How could I be when I work for *her?* *(He dries his tears with the handkerchief.)*

LUCY. Her? Who?

TUMNUS. The White Witch, that's who. Oh, she calls herself a queen, but she's the evil ruler of Narnia. She's the one who makes it always winter here. But she never lets us have Christmas.

LUCY. What kind of work do you do for the witch?

TUMNUS. I'm a kidnapper. I'm supposed to kidnap innocent children and bring them to her.

LUCY. I'm sure you wouldn't do anything of the sort.

TUMNUS. But I am doing it—at this very moment. *(He moves toward her. She recoils.)*

LUCY *(frightened)*. What do you mean?

TUMNUS. I'm suppose to take you to the witch. *(He takes her arm firmly, but gently.)*

LUCY. But you won't, will you, Mr. Tumnus?

TUMNUS. If I don't turn you over to the White Witch, she'll cut off my tail, saw off my horns, pluck out my beard—and worse, she'll turn me into a stone statue with her magic wand.

LUCY. Maybe she won't know I was here. Will you please let me go home? *(After a moment, he releases her.)*

TUMNUS. Of course I will. I didn't know what a human was like before I met you. But now that I know you, I can't give you up to the witch. I'll take you back to the lamppost. From there you can find your way back to War Drobe in the land of Spare Oom.

LUCY *(deeply relieved)*. Thank you, Mr. Tumnus.

TUMNUS. We must go as quietly as we can. The woods are full of her spies. *(They leave his "home" cautiously.*

He looks about, then speaks in a low voice.) Can you
ever forgive me for what I meant to do?

LUCY. Of course. And I hope you won't get into dreadful trouble on my account. *(She starts to exit off, R.)*

TUMNUS *(waving the handkerchief toward her).* Farewell,
Daughter of Eve. Oh, may I keep your handkerchief as
a reminder of our pleasant visit?

LUCY. Certainly. *(She waves and exits.)*

TUMNUS *(creeping back toward his "home" and enter-
ing).* I hope none of her spies saw me. I feel ever so
much better about everything. Starting now I'm going
to turn over a new leaf. I'm going to be a much better—

(FENRIS ULF enters. He rushes into Tumnus' "home.")

ULF. Ah, ha! *(TUMNUS drops to his knees trembling.)*

TUMNUS. Oh, no.

ULF. Tumnus, your treachery has been detected. You
had a human in your very grasp and let her go. *(He
grabs TUMNUS roughly and brings him to his feet.)* The
Queen will deal with you—Tumnus the traitor! *(He
breaks a piece of furniture.)* I order this house destroyed! You won't be needing it any longer, betrayer
of the Queen.

*(The WOOD NYMPHS enter and quickly disassemble
the "home," then exit with the pieces.)*

ULF. This document will serve notice to other traitors
who may have the same notion as you. *(He hangs a
note on a nearby tree branch, or simply lets the note fall
to the ground where the "home" was.)* Come, Tumnus.

Soon your name will be written in stone—your very
own! *(He laughs menacingly and exits, dragging TUM-
NUS with him.)*

EDMUND'S VOICE *(off).* Lucy, you're crazy. It's just a
big, old wardrobe like any other big, old wardrobe with
lots of coats inside. It's stuffy—and dark—and cold.

(EDMUND enters.)

EDMUND. Cold? It was warm in the wardrobe. *(He is
astonished at his new surroundings.)*

(LUCY enters.)

LUCY. But now we're in Narnia.

EDMUND. Narnia?

LUCY. You didn't believe me. I wanted to tell Peter and
Susan as well. But you were the first one I found. And
I wanted to get back here as soon as possible.

EDMUND. I thought you were teasing, but I guess you
were right after all.

LUCY. Now the first thing we must do is see if Mr. Tumnus, the faun, is safe. I hope the White Witch didn't
get him.

EDMUND. Witch? There's a witch here in Narnia?

LUCY. An evil witch who has a magic so that it's always
winter in Narnia—but never Christmas. *(Looking
about.)* Now where on earth—I mean, in Narnia—is
Mr. Tumnus' home? I thought it was right over there.
We have to go look for him. Come, Edmund.

EDMUND. I'll stay right here, thank you. I have no de-
sire to go traipsing off after some silly faun. I'll be here
at the lamppost—*if* I stay. I'm not sure I like it here.

LUCY. Please don't leave without me. I'll be right back after I make sure Mr. Tumnus is okay. *(She exits.)*

EDMUND. Narnia, eh? I didn't believe Lucy, but she was right. It's a fascinating place, I'll admit. But all this business about fauns and witches and — *(The sounds of harness bells are heard off, followed by the voice of the WITCH. EDMUND quickly tries to hide behind a tree or the lamppost.)*

WITCH'S VOICE *(off)*. Hold there! Tie the reindeer to that tree, Dwarf.

DWARF'S VOICE *(off)*. Yes, majesty. Consider it done.

WITCH'S VOICE *(off)*. Now, let us follow the smell of the intruder.

(The DWARF and WITCH, who carries a wand, enter and see the cowering EDMUND.)

DWARF. You there!

EDMUND *(very frightened)*. Who? Me?

DWARF. Yes, you! Kneel in the presence of the mighty ruler of Narnia.

EDMUND. But — but I am kneeling.

DWARF. Lower! *(EDMUND falls prostrate to the ground.)* That's more like it.

WITCH. What, pray, are you?

EDMUND. I'm — I'm — my name is Edmund.

WITCH. Is that how you address a queen?

EDMUND. I'm — I'm sorry... your majesty. I thought you were — a witch.

WITCH. A witch? *(She laughs loudly.)* *I* am a queen. The Queen of Narnia. Now, I repeat — what are *you?*

EDMUND. I'm — I'm a boy — *(Adding quickly.)* — your majesty.

WITCH. A boy. A boy? Did you hear that, Dwarf? A boy.

DWARF. He must be — a Son of Adam.

WITCH. He looks more like an idiot. Tell me — boy, how did you enter my dominion?

EDMUND. Through a wardrobe, your majesty. I'm not sure exactly how it happened, but in an instant I was here.

WITCH. A wardrobe? A passageway from the other world? The world of men! This could ruin everything. It could even be the beginning of the dreaded prophesy — unless — *(Her attitude suddenly changes toward EDMUND.)* My poor child. How cold you look. *(She helps him up and puts her arm around him.)* Dwarf, bring him something warm to drink. *(The DWARF exits.)*

EDMUND. Thank you, your majesty.

WITCH. Tell me, Edmund, my dear — Son of Adam — are there any more of you — *humans,* I mean — in these parts?

EDMUND. I have a sister, Lucy, who's looking for a faun.

WITCH. Ah, she must be the Daughter of Eve who escaped from that fool Tumnus. Well, let's see — you and Lucy, you say. That's only two humans. The prophesy said there would be four. So, there's nothing to worry about unless... You don't have any other brothers or sisters do you?

EDMUND. Yes. Peter and Susan.

WITCH *(alarmed).* What? Where are they?

EDMUND. Still in the house where we're visiting... on the other side of the wardrobe.

WITCH *(counting on her fingers).* Edmund, Lucy, Peter and Susan. Two Sons of Adam — two Daughters of Eve.

That's four—just as the prophesy has stated. This is horrible!

EDMUND. What's wrong, your majesty?

WITCH *(catching herself, then sweetly)*. Oh, nothing. Nothing at all. I just meant—it's *horrible* that your dear brother and sisters aren't here with us now. I would take all of you to my castle. I would make them the Duke and Duchesses of this land. But you, dear Edmund—because you are special and I found you first—I would make you the Prince of Narnia.

EDMUND. Really?

WITCH. And someday you would be *King.*

EDMUND *(excited)*. King? You mean it?

(The DWARF enters with a fancy copper bottle and a jewelled cup.)

WITCH. Ah, here is your delightful drink. Sweet and creamy and delicious. *(The DWARF pours the drink for EDMUND who tastes it.)*

EDMUND. It's wonderful.

WITCH. And you must have a little something to eat as well. What is your favorite candy?

EDMUND. Oh, that's easy. Turkish Delight.

WITCH. Then Turkish Delight it shall be. *(Almost magically, the WITCH produces a small colorful candy box which she opens and offers to EDMUND. He takes a piece of candy and eats it.)* Enjoy, my little prince.

EDMUND. It's the best Turkish Delight I've ever tasted. May I have more?

WITCH *(closing the box)*. Of course. Back at my castle. I have rooms filled with Turkish Delight.

EDMUND. Then let's go there right now.

WITCH. First, you must fetch the others.

EDMUND. I can bring them another time.

WITCH. *Now* — my dear. Bring them to my castle. It's between those two hills. You can't miss it. You'll smell the Turkish Delight all the way. *(She laughs seductively.)* Come, Dwarf, we must prepare for our esteemed guests. *(The DWARF laughs derisively as he and the WITCH start to leave.)* Oh, Edmund, my precious. Don't tell the others about me just yet. I want them to be — surprised — when they see me. Let's keep this visit our little secret. *(She holds the candy box aloft tantalizingly as she and the DWARF exit.)*

WITCH'S VOICE *(off)*. Don't spare the whip on the reindeer, Dwarf. We have much to do in a short time. *(Harness bells are heard fading in the distance.)*

EDMUND *(ecstatically)*. Turkish Delight! Rooms filled with it! Yes, I will bring Lucy and Peter and Susan to the Queen. *(A pause.)* I'm glad she told me she was a queen — or else, I might have mistaken her for a witch.

(LUCY enters.)

LUCY. Edmund, this is terrible. I can't find Mr. Tumnus anywhere.

EDMUND. Perhaps we should go get Peter and Susan to help us find him.

LUCY *(pleased)*. You really want to? I didn't think you liked it here.

EDMUND. Maybe the place does deserve a second look after all. Especially that large castle between those two hills.

LUCY. Good. We'll go get Peter and Susan.

EDMUND. And this time we'll get some coats out of the wardrobe. It's cold here.

LUCY. As I told you, it's all the witch's fault.

EDMUND. Oh, go on, Lucy. There's no such thing as a witch in Narnia.

(They exit. A moment later, MR. and MRS. BEAVER enter.)

MR. BEAVER. The broken dam will just have to wait.

MRS. BEAVER. Yes. This other business is much more important. *(Looking offstage.)* Look, there's the Unicorn. We will tell him.

MR. BEAVER. Mr. Unicorn. Over here if you will.

(UNICORN enters.)

UNICORN. Oh, good. It's you. I was afraid it was that awful Fenris Ulf.

MR. BEAVER. He left some time ago.

MRS. BEAVER. Dragging the unfortunate Mr. Tumnus with him.

UNICORN. How do you know?

MR. BEAVER. They passed right by us. We hid behind the dam.

MRS. BEAVER. Fenris Ulf didn't see us, but Mr. Tumnus did. And he dropped this so we would find it. *(She holds up Lucy's handkerchief.)*

UNICORN. What is it?

MR. BEAVER *(taking the handkerchief from MRS. BEAVER).* We're not sure, but we believe it belongs to a human.

MRS. BEAVER. It has the smell of a Daughter of Eve.

UNICORN. You think that a human has been here?

MR. BEAVER. Yes, and that Tumnus let her go. That's why he was in such trouble with Fenris Ulf.

UNICORN. So where is this human now—if there was one?

MRS. BEAVER. Who knows?

UNICORN. If she's smart, she left Narnia the minute she had the chance. Never to return.

MR. BEAVER. *Or* to return with others.

UNICORN. Others? You mean humans?

MRS. BEAVER. Perhaps. Remember the prophesy.

UNICORN *(thinking out loud)*. Two Sons of Adam—and two Daughters of Eve. Is it possible?

MR. BEAVER. Who knows? We'll just have to wait and see.

(CENTAUR enters.)

CENTAUR. Listen! I just heard the most wonderful news. They say *He* has arrived in these parts.

MRS. BEAVER. Our King?

CENTAUR. Yes. And that He is on the move. They say he will likely appear at the Stone Table any time now.

UNICORN. This *is* wonderful news.

MRS. BEAVER. Mr. Centaur, we are expecting the arrival of children—*human* children. They could be here at any minute. If they reach *Him*, the prophesy will be fulfilled.

CENTAUR. But what if the witch gets to them first?

MRS. BEAVER. We must protect the children from the moment they arrive until they reach the Stone Table.

UNICORN. And keep them hidden from the witch.

MR. BEAVER. Exactly.

CENTAUR. But which of us can help them? They might be afraid of me.

UNICORN. They might not trust *me*. Unicorns are only make-believe in their world.

CENTAUR. Mr. and Mrs. Beaver, will you help them — protect them from danger?

MR. BEAVER. But — but — *(The voices of LUCY, EDMUND, PETER and SUSAN are heard off.)*

VOICES *(off)*. It's this way. Come on. I still don't believe you. It's here somewhere. Look for the lamppost. *(Etc.)*

CENTAUR. They're coming. Will you please take care of them?

MR. BEAVER. But — but —

MRS. BEAVER. Of course. I'll prepare some food for dinner. *(She exits.)*

UNICORN. Mr. Centaur, let us go and see if the good news you have heard is true.

CENTAUR. Yes, let us go immediately. *(He and the UNICORN exit.)*

MR. BEAVER *(to himself)*. But — but — what if the children are afraid of me, too — or don't trust me? I'd better hide until I can get my wits together. *(He exits.)*

VOICES OF THE CHILDREN *(off)*. Just a little further. That's it. Are you sure it's this way? Yes, I see the lamppost. Follow me. *(Etc.)*

(LUCY and EDMUND enter, followed by PETER and SUSAN. All are wearing overcoats too large for them.)

LUCY *(triumphantly)*. Now are you convinced, Peter?

PETER. Yes. I apologize, Lu, for not believing you.

SUSAN. It's so...different. And it's also very cold.

LUCY. That's why we borrowed these coats from the wardrobe, Susan.

PETER. Well, what do we do first?

EDMUND. Explore, of course. *(Pointing in the distance toward the witch's castle.)* Let's go in that direction.

LUCY. Don't forget where the lamppost is. That's our landmark. We'll need to find it when we wish to return home.

SUSAN. I think we should go back home now. It's scary here.

PETER. Don't be such a goose, Susan. Where's your sense of adventure?

LUCY. Whether we stay here or not, we must at least find poor Mr. Tumnus.

EDMUND. But you tried already. You couldn't even find his house.

LUCY. I would have sworn it was right over here. *(She goes to where Tumnus' "home" was, followed by the OTHERS.)*

SUSAN *(pointing to the note left by FENRIS ULF)*. Look. What's that?

PETER *(picking up the note)*. A message of some kind. *(He reads.)* "The former occupant of these premises, Faun Tumnus, is under arrest and awaiting his trial on a charge of high treason against her Imperial Majesty Jadis, Queen of Narnia."

SUSAN *(looking over Peter's shoulder, she continues reading)*. "Signed, Fenris Ulf, Captain of the Secret Police. Long live the Queen."

LUCY. Oh, no.

PETER. Who is this queen, Lu?

LUCY. She isn't a real queen at all. She's a horrible witch who makes it always winter and never Christmas in Narnia.

SUSAN. It doesn't seem safe here. What about just going home?

LUCY. But we must try to rescue Mr. Tumnus. It's my fault he's in trouble.

PETER. I suppose Lu is right.

SUSAN. Very well. But this place worries me.

PETER. Where should we look first?

EDMUND. I think we should look for something to eat.

PETER. Oh, you're always thinking about your stomach.

EDMUND. And you're always thinking about your clothes and your hair and how you look. *(He shoves PETER slightly.)*

PETER *(pushing EDMUND back)*. Well, if I looked like you—

SUSAN. Please, you two. Stop acting like—brothers.

LUCY. I just wish I knew where Mr. Tumnus was imprisoned.

EDMUND. Why don't we go toward that castle—between those two hills?

LUCY. Very well.

SUSAN. Perhaps it will be warmer there. *(They start to leave but are stopped by a thumping sound offstage.)*

PETER. What was that?

EDMUND. Nothing, scaredy-cat. Let's go. *(Another thumping sound is heard.)*

SUSAN *(afraid)*. Who—who's there?

(MR. BEAVER enters.)

MR. BEAVER. Are you the Sons of Adam and the Daughters of Eve?

PETER (*a bit nervous*). We're—some of them.

MR. BEAVER. Quick, follow me. We are not safe here.

LUCY. What do you mean?

MR. BEAVER. Many of the forest creatures are our friends, but some are on *her* side, if you know what I mean. Come, let us go.

EDMUND. Wait a minute. I say we head for the castle. Who wants to listen to a silly beaver?

PETER. Stop being so smug, Ed, and pay attention to him.

EDMUND. How do we know he's a friend?

MR. BEAVER. Here is my token. (*He shows them Lucy's handkerchief.*)

LUCY. My handkerchief!

MR. BEAVER. Mr. Tumnus dropped it so that we would know to expect you. Now please come quickly. We must get you safely to our King.

SUSAN. Your king?

MR. BEAVER. Aslan!

LUCY (*reverently*). Aslan.

SUSAN (*somewhat awed*). Aslan.

PETER. The very name makes me feel brave and adventurous.

SUSAN. The name sounds like a delightful strain of music to me.

LUCY. It warms me up—makes me feel like summer.

EDMUND (*almost to himself*). It gives me a bad feeling—like some mysterious horror.

PETER. Ed, what is wrong with you? You're acting so strangely.

EDMUND. How else are you supposed to act in a strange place? I say we go to the castle.

PETER. I say we go with Mr. Beaver.

LUCY. I, too.

SUSAN. And I.

PETER. Three against one, Ed. Come on. *(MR. BEAVER leads them to his "home.")*

MR. BEAVER. Mrs. Beaver, we're here! I found them — the Sons of Adam and the Daughters of Eve!

(MRS. BEAVER enters with armloads of food as the OTHERS go into the Beavers' "home.")

MRS. BEAVER *(setting the food on the table)*. Welcome. I have some dinner for you. Fresh from the smoke-house outside.

SUSAN. Umm. It looks delicious.

LUCY. Yes, indeed. I'm famished.

PETER. We're very grateful for your hospitality — *(Gouging the sullen EDMUND.)* — aren't we, Ed.

EDMUND. I prefer Turkish Delight.

MRS. BEAVER. What, dear?

PETER. He said it looks — *perfect.* He's *delighted. (He glares at EDMUND.)*

MR. BEAVER. Before we eat, let us each say a word of thanks — and hope — for the coming events. *(ALL except EDMUND bow their heads and pray silently for a moment.)* Good. Now enjoy the meal. *(They begin to eat. EDMUND merely toys with his food.)*

MRS. BEAVER. How very honored we are to have the children of the prophesy.

SUSAN. What do you mean — "children of the proph-esy"?

LUCY. I'm not even sure what "prophesy" means.

PETER. It's something that's predicted, Lu. Something that will probably happen.

LUCY. Oh. What exactly is the prophesy, Mr. Beaver?

MR. BEAVER. It is told in the form of a rhyme —
"Wrong will be right when Aslan comes in sight.
At the sound of his roar, sorrows will be no more.
When he bears his teeth, winter will meet its death.
And when he shakes his mane, we shall have spring again."

LUCY. Who is Aslan — a man?

MR. BEAVER. Certainly not. He is King of the Wood and Son of the Great Emperor Beyond the Sea. Aslan is a lion — the Great Lion. And we have heard that he may be in Narnia even as we speak. If it is true, we will take you to the Stone Table early in the morning so that you may meet him.

MRS. BEAVER. And help fulfill the prophesy.

PETER. But — how do *we* fit into all this?

SUSAN. We still don't understand about the prophesy.

MR. BEAVER. But you will. Listen to the rest of the rhyme —
"When Adam's flesh and Adam's bone
Sits at Cair Paravel in throne,
The evil time will be over and done."

LUCY. What does that mean — "Adam's flesh and Adam's bone"?

MR. BEAVER. It means humans.

MRS. BEAVER. You're the first humans ever to come to Narnia.

EDMUND. But what about the Queen — and the Dwarf? Aren't they human?

MR. BEAVER. You mean the *Witch* and the Dwarf. She'd like you to believe they're human, but they're not. They're evil through and through. Not a drop of human blood in them.

PETER. This Cair Paravel that you mentioned — how many thrones are there?

MR. BEAVER. Four. Two for the Sons of Adam —

MRS. BEAVER. — and two for the Daughters of Eve.

MR. BEAVER. And when they are filled, it will mean the end of the witch's reign — and her life. *(As they ponder the meaning of this, EDMUND slips unnoticed out of the "home" and exits.)*

PETER. Two — and two.

MR. BEAVER. *You* are the four.

SUSAN. It's quite a responsibility.

MR. BEAVER. It's quite a necessity. Can we count on you to help fulfill the prophesy —

MRS. BEAVER. — even though the adventure will be filled with danger? *(A pause.)*

PETER. I, for one, am ready.

LUCY. I, too.

SUSAN. And I.

PETER. What about you, Ed?

SUSAN. Ed?

LUCY. Edmund? *(They see the empty chair.)*

MRS. BEAVER. Where could he have gone?

SUSAN. Perhaps to get some air.

LUCY. Do you think he became ill? He hasn't looked well since we got here.

PETER. Wait a minute. He mentioned the witch — and also a *dwarf*. We knew nothing of a dwarf. Is there such a person?

MR. BEAVER. Yes. He drives the witch's sleigh.

PETER. That means Ed has met them.

MRS. BEAVER. And eaten her food, no doubt. He had that look. He is surely under her spell.

MR. BEAVER. He's probably well on his way to her castle by now.

PETER. Then we must go there and stop him.

MR. BEAVER. No. You mustn't go near the witch.

MRS. BEAVER. She would turn you all to stone with her magic wand.

PETER. But we have to get Ed back. All four of us are needed to fulfill the prophesy.

SUSAN. What shall we do?

MR. BEAVER. If Aslan is indeed in Narnia, we can ask him what to do.

MRS. BEAVER. Then we shall set out for the Stone Table first thing tomorrow.

MR. BEAVER. I say we set out right now. When Edmund tells the witch where we are, she'll come here and turn us all to stone. *(Harness bells are heard, off.)*

VOICE *(off)*. This is the place all right!

MRS. BEAVER. Oh, no.

LUCY. Is that—?

MRS. BEAVER. I'm afraid so.

MR. BEAVER. It seems the witch has arrived already. There's no time for escape. Be brave, young friends.

(An ELF enters and stands at the door.)

ELF. You in there—make yourselves presentable to an esteemed visitor.

SUSAN. It's the dwarf.

ELF. I resent that insinuation. I'm no dwarf. I'm an *elf*.

PETER. What's the difference? Either way, the witch is going to come in and—

LUCY. Wait a minute, Peter. There *is* a difference. *(To the ELF.)* An elf, you say?

ELF. An elf, I said.

LUCY. Elves aren't bad at all, if I'm not mistaken.

ELF. You're not mistaken. *(Referring to PETER.)* He's mistaken. *(To LUCY.)* You're Lucy.

LUCY. And you're clever—very clever, because you know my name.

ELF. I know.

LUCY. And you could only know my name—*all* of our names—if you travel with the one who knows *everybody's* name—

ELF. Name him.

LUCY. Father Christmas! *(She and the ELF join hands and dance about laughing as the OTHERS cheer.)*

MRS. BEAVER. Do you mean that Father Christmas is actually here?

MR. BEAVER. After all these years?

ELF. In the flesh. Or in the fur, as it were. Tah-dah!

(FATHER CHRISTMAS enters carrying a filled burlap bag over his shoulder. NOTE: FATHER CHRISTMAS is attired in furry, festive, yet somewhat rustic, clothing. He should not appear as a contemporary Santa Claus.)

ALL. Father Christmas!

FATHER CHRISTMAS. I've come at last. The powers of the witch have kept me away for some time. But lately I've felt stronger—more like myself. That's why I'm making my rounds again.

MRS. BEAVER. They say that Aslan is on the move.

FATHER CHRISTMAS. That must be the answer. Well, are you ready for your gifts? First, Mr. Beaver, I have repaired your dam and mended the leak.

MR. BEAVER (*overwhelmed*). Why, I—I—

ELF. A simple "thank you" will suffice.

MR. BEAVER. Thank you.

FATHER CHRISTMAS. And Mrs. Beaver, in the room next to the smokehouse, I've left for you a brand new sewing machine.

MRS. BEAVER (*delighted*). Oh, my—I—I—

ELF (*pointing to MR. BEAVER*). What he said.

MRS. BEAVER. Thank you.

FATHER CHRISTMAS. Peter, Son of Adam.

PETER. Yes, sir.

FATHER CHRISTMAS (*taking items from his bag*). These are your presents. They are tools, not toys. The time to use them is perhaps near at hand. (*He holds up a shield and a sword.*) The sword and shield are yours. Bear them well. (*PETER receives the gifts solemnly and silently bows to acknowledge his appreciation.*) Susan, Daughter of Eve. (*SUSAN steps forward.*) These are for you. (*He hands her a bow and a quiver of arrows.*) Use the bow only in great need. (*Giving her a hunting horn.*) Blow this horn when you are in trouble, and help of some kind will come to you.

SUSAN. Thank you, sir.

FATHER CHRISTMAS. Lucy, younger Daughter of Eve. (*He holds up a small glass bottle.*) In this bottle is a cordial made from the juice of fire-flowers. If you or your friends are ever hurt, a few drops will restore you. (*He takes out a dagger.*) And this dagger is to defend yourself. But use it only when absolutely necessary. (*He gives the items to LUCY.*)

LUCY. Thank you, Father Christmas.

FATHER CHRISTMAS. Well, we must be on our way. We have many more stops tonight. It's wonderful to be working again. A Merry Christmas to all of you. And long live the true King.

ALL. Long live the true King! *(FATHER CHRISTMAS and the ELF exit.)*

MR. BEAVER. And we, too, must be on *our* way. We must travel quietly and cautiously. The witch's spies are everywhere. The gifts of Father Christmas may well be needed before this journey is over. Come, let us go.

(They exit. The WOOD NYMPHS enter and quickly remove the set pieces of the Beavers' "home" from the stage. They also remove the lamppost. A moment later, they bring out two or three set pieces suggesting the courtyard of the witch. After the WOOD NYMPHS exit, EDMUND enters the courtyard somewhat exhausted.)

FENRIS ULF'S VOICE *(off)*. Who's there? Who goes there?

(ULF enters.)

ULF. Who are you stranger?

EDMUND. If you please, sir, my name is Edmund. I am a Son of Adam. I bring news of my brother and sisters. The Queen wanted to see them.

ULF. Very well. I shall tell her majesty. Meanwhile, stand still if you value your life, or you will be turned to stone like the others in the outer courtyard.

EDMUND. You mean those statues out there used to be alive?

ULF. Yes, until they crossed her majesty and paid the price. An enemy of the Queen ultimately becomes a statue of stone. *(He laughs menacingly and exits.)*

EDMUND *(nervously, trying to reassure himself)*. Well, I'm sure they were all bad to the Queen or she wouldn't have turned them into statues. She was certainly nice to me. Nicer, I'll bet, than that old Aslan, or whatever his name is. I'm sure the others will like the Queen. She said she would make Peter a duke — and Lucy and Susan duchesses. But *I'll* be the prince — and someday the *king*. I'm going to love it here — staying with a Queen who is so kind and good.

WITCH'S VOICE *(off)*. Where is the little fool?

(The WITCH enters, followed by ULF and the DWARF.)

WITCH. How dare you come alone! Did I not tell you to bring the others?

EDMUND *(frightened)*. I did the best I could, your majesty. I just wanted you to know they're here in Narnia. I'm sure I can bring them to you after they've been to see Aslan. *(The WITCH screams.)*

WITCH. Never speak that name in my presence again.

EDMUND *(shaken)*. Yes, your majesty.

WITCH. So, he has arrived, has he?

ULF. Perhaps it's only a rumor, your majesty.

WITCH. No. It must be true. Everything seems to be getting warmer. Even the snows in the fields are starting to melt. Where are your brother and sisters right now?

EDMUND. They *were* at the home of the Beavers. But they may be on their way to the Stone Table to meet As—uh, to meet *Him*.

WITCH. We must capture the children before they reach that creature.

EDMUND. Capture? But why?

WITCH. Quiet, you! I shall never allow the prophesy to come true. Never! Dwarf, make ready the sleigh for our journey. We must leave immediately.

DWARF. Your majesty, I'm afraid we'll have to walk. The reindeer cannot travel without snow. They'll sink into the mud.

WITCH. Then we shall go on foot. Fenris Ulf, Chief of my Secret Police, you are the fleetest of all my army. Go ahead of us. Overtake the humans before they reach the Stone Table. Kill anything in your path—especially the Beavers for harboring the enemy.

ULF *(bowing deeply)*. I hear and obey, my Queen. *(He exits quickly.)*

WITCH. Dwarf, tie the hands of this human behind his back and drive him ahead of us with your whip.

DWARF. With pleasure, your majesty. *(He begins to tie Edmund's hands with a piece of rope.)*

EDMUND. But—but—your majesty, what about my Turkish Delight? You said—

WITCH. Silence, fool.

EDMUND. But I'm hungry.

WITCH. Enough of this stalling. We must be off. Move! Move!

(The DWARF cracks his whip, as EDMUND, in tears, exits, followed offstage by the DWARF and WITCH. Mo-

ments later, the BEAVERS, PETER, SUSAN and LUCY enter at the other side of the stage.)

LUCY *(pointing toward the sky)*. Look, there's a king-fisher.

SUSAN. What is that lovely smell?

MRS. BEAVER. Can it actually be Spring flowers?

MR. BEAVER. No doubt about it. Spring is in the air.

PETER. It must be getting warmer. When we stopped for a rest back in the meadow, we took our coats off and forgot to put them back on.

LUCY *(realizing they are not wearing their coats)*. So we did.

SUSAN. Shh. Listen. *(Melodic humming or chanting, accompanied by stringed instruments, is heard UC.)*

PETER. Look!

(ASLAN, a great lion, enters. He is surrounded by his FOLLOWERS, animals of the forest. The CENTAUR and UNICORN are among them.)

FOLLOWERS. Aslan! Aslan! Aslan! All hail—Aslan! *(He embraces them as they move to the Stone Table.)*

MRS. BEAVER. He's here. He's here at last.

MR. BEAVER *(to PETER)*. Go speak to him.

PETER. No, you first.

MR. BEAVER. Sons of Adam before animals.

PETER *(somewhat reluctantly)*. Very well. *(He puts the sword under his arm, military fashion.)* Come on, everybody. Let's go. *(They advance slowly, in awe, toward ASLAN. PETER speaks a bit nervously.)* Aslan—we have come. *(They kneel.)*

ASLAN. Welcome, Peter, Son of Adam. Welcome, Susan and Lucy, Daughters of Eve. Welcome He-Beaver and She-Beaver. But...where is the other Son of Adam?

MR. BEAVER. He has tried to betray his brother and sisters and has joined the White Witch, O Aslan.

PETER. It was partly my fault, Aslan. We were arguing. That may have pushed him in the wrong direction.

LUCY. Please – Aslan. Can anything be done to save Edmund?

ASLAN. All shall be done. But it may be harder than you think. Meanwhile, let a feast of celebration be prepared in yon pavilion. You will find food and drink in abundance there. *(ALL react favorably as they start to leave.)* Peter and I shall join you momentarily. *(He puts his arm around PETER as the OTHERS exit.)* Son of Adam.

PETER. Yes, Aslan?

ASLAN. Look far into the distance where Narnia meets the sea. There is a castle.

PETER. I can see it.

ASLAN. It is Cair Paravel of the four thrones. If the prophesy is to be fulfilled, you, your brother and your sisters shall sit in those thrones.

PETER. Yes. Mr. and Mrs. Beaver explained it to us. But don't all four of us have to sit together?

ASLAN. Yes.

PETER. Then what about Edmund? What if the White Witch – *(A loud trumpet-like sound is heard on a horn offstage.)* What was that?

ASLAN. Your sister's horn.

PETER. Father Christmas told her to blow it when there was trouble. Something dreadful must be –

(SUSAN and the OTHERS enter, retreating in fear.)

PETER. What is it, Susan?

SUSAN. A monster!

1ST ANIMAL. He's coming this way!

2ND ANIMAL. He's right behind us.

PETER. Can you tell who — or what — it is? *(ALL look off in the direction from where they entered.)*

3RD ANIMAL. It looks to be —

4TH ANIMAL. I'm afraid it is —

5TH ANIMAL. Fenris Ulf. Captain of the Witch's Secret Police.

PETER. Aslan, will you protect us from him?

ASLAN. No, but *you* will.

PETER. Me? *(ALL express concern.)*

ASLAN. Stand back! Let the Prince win his spurs.

(ALL form a semi-circle U away from PETER as ULF enters.)

ULF. Well — *(Mockingly.)* — so the great Aslan *has* returned. My Queen will be interested in this news. But before I go, would the "mighty one" like to test my strength? *(ASLAN motions toward PETER who reluctantly, nervously holds up his sword and shield. ULF laughs scornfully.)* Are you so afraid of Fenris Ulf that you designate a mere mortal to fight in your stead? Well, I shall make short work of him — just as my Queen's army will dispatch you and your cowardly crew in the wink of an eye. *(With a ferocious growl, he lunges toward PETER, knocking him to the ground. PETER quickly regains his composure and the two fight fiercely. After a long struggle, PETER plunges his sword into ULF who howls and holds his wound, exiting in the direction from which he came. The OTHERS cheer PETER who is weary and exhausted.)*

ASLAN. Well done, my son. You have given the beast a mortal wound. But let us hope he reaches the witch before he dies. *(ALL are puzzled.)*

1ST ANIMAL. But why, O Aslan?

ASLAN. So that all of you can follow him and rescue the other Son of Adam. *(ALL express reluctance to do so.)* Do not fear. Your strength will be in your numbers — and also in your faith to accomplish the task. *(ALL agree.)* The children will stay here with me.

ALL *(as they leave)*. I think he went in that direction. Here is a trail of blood. He turned north at that grove of trees. Quickly follow him. *(Etc. They exit.)*

ASLAN *(to PETER)*. You have forgotten to clean your sword. *(PETER wipes each side of the blade on the ground.)* Now, hand it to me and kneel, Son of Adam. *(He takes the sword as PETER kneels. He strikes PETER on each shoulder with the flat of the blade.)* Rise up, Sir Peter Fenris-Bane. Your new name will tell the world that you were the destroyer of the evil wolf. Always maintain your courage. And whatever happens, never forget to wipe your sword.

PETER. Yes, Aslan.

ASLAN. And now, let us go to the pavilion to await the others. If all goes well, they will return with your brother.

(They exit. A moment later, EDMUND, who is exhausted, and the DWARF, who drives him with the whip, enter. The WITCH enters close behind.)

WITCH. It will be difficult to reach the Stone Table before the humans do—unless they were delayed along the way. Surely Fenris Ulf will bring word to us soon.

EDMUND *(dropping to his knees)*. Please—your majesty—may we rest—just a bit?

WITCH. No, you young fool, we must continue to move ahead. I said move!

(The DWARF raises his whip to strike EDMUND, but stops when ULF enters stumbling and collapses at the feet of the WITCH.)

WITCH. What's this?

ULF *(struggling to speak)*. Your...majesty.

WITCH. Fenris Ulf! Who has done this horrible thing to you?

ULF. The other... Son of Adam... at the bidding of As—As—

WITCH. No! Do not dare to speak his name.

ULF. But he...is here...at the Stone Table. *(The WITCH screams.)* Now let me go into yonder thicket...where I may rest...forever. *(He drags himself along the ground.)*

WITCH *(in agony)*. Fenris Ulf! My Captain. They have slain him. *(ULF exits.)*

DWARF *(nervously)*. Now the prophesy will surely come true.

WITCH *(with resolve)*. No! There are four thrones in Cair Paravel. If only three are occupied, the prophesy can never be fulfilled, and *He* can never rule over Narnia.

DWARF. Then we had better do what we have to do at once.

WITCH. Prepare the victim. *(The DWARF pushes EDMUND prostrate to the ground.)*

EDMUND *(in great fear)*. No, please... what are you going to do to me?

WITCH. The very same that your wretched brother did to my beloved Captain. *(She takes out a dagger and raises it above her head. Suddenly, offstage VOICES are heard.)*

VOICES *(off)*. There they are! Quick! After them! *(Etc.)*

WITCH. What is that?

DWARF. The Forces of Aslan!

WITCH. We are outnumbered. Quick, we must disappear.

(The WITCH and the DWARF quickly hide behind trees as the OTHERS enter in a rush.)

ALL. Is he dead? He's all right. He only fainted. Where are the Witch and the Dwarf? Quick, let us get the boy back to Aslan. *(Etc. They lift EDMUND and carry him as they exit. The WITCH and DWARF slowly come out of hiding.)*

WITCH *(with anger and determination)*. Very well, my old adversary—Aslan. Aslan... yes, I *can* speak the name, for he will soon be mine. The Deep Magic is on my side. Perhaps he has forgotten the Deep Magic, but I shall remind him. *(A pause.)* Dwarf, we must summon our allies to meet us as soon as possible. Call the Ghouls, the Boggles, the Ogres. Bring forth the Cruels, the Spectres, the Hags. This is war! And we shall fight with one aim in mind—to end forever the name of Aslan! *(They exit quickly.)*

(NOTE: An intermission may occur at this point if desired.)

(ASLAN, PETER, SUSAN and LUCY enter.)

PETER. I'm worried, Aslan. We should have gone with the others to help rescue Ed. *(He lifts his sword.)*

ASLAN. No, we cannot chance losing *more* children of Adam and Eve. I have every confidence in those who followed the wolf. *(The voices of a CROWD are heard offstage.)*

SUSAN. Listen...they're coming back!

LUCY. Is Edmund with them?

PETER. I can't tell...Yes, I think he is!

(The OTHERS enter. They set EDMUND down. Unsteadily, he gains his footing. LUCY, SUSAN and PETER rush to him.)

LUCY. Edmund!

SUSAN. What happened?

PETER. Ed, are you all right?

EDMUND. The Queen—I mean, the Witch—she—she—it was awful. *(He cries. ASLAN goes to him and gently puts his arm around him.)*

ASLAN. It's all right, my son. You are among friends now.

EDMUND *(in awe)*. You're...Aslan?

ASLAN. Yes. Come with me for a moment. *(He takes EDMUND aside. In a soft voice, unheard by the OTHERS, he gently lectures to EDMUND.)*

1ST ANIMAL. What is he saying to the boy?

MRS. BEAVER. Whatever it is, it will be the right and proper thing.

LUCY. I wish I could hear.

MR. BEAVER. It's only for them to know.

MRS. BEAVER. Whatever Aslan is telling him, the boy will never forget it. *(ASLAN and EDMUND return to the OTHERS.)*

ASLAN. Here is your brother. There is no need to talk to him about what is past.

EDMUND. I'm sorry, Lu. *(He embraces LUCY.)*

LUCY. It's all right, Edmund.

EDMUND. Susan. *(He embraces SUSAN.)*

SUSAN. We're glad you're safe.

EDMUND. Peter. *(Shaking hands with PETER.)*

PETER. Welcome back...brother.

1ST ANIMAL. Look, someone is coming.

ASLAN. See who approaches. *(The 1ST ANIMAL exits.)*

PETER *(drawing his sword)*. Shall we prepare for battle again?

ASLAN. Hold, my son. We shall see what comes to pass.

2ND ANIMAL. Look! The intruder carries a white flag.

3RD ANIMAL. The sign of peace.

(The 1ST ANIMAL enters.)

1ST ANIMAL. Sire, there is a messenger from the enemy who craves an audience with you.

ASLAN. Let him approach.

(The 1ST ANIMAL motions offstage. The DWARF enters carrying a white flag.)

ASLAN. You appear to come in peace. What is your message?

DWARF. The Queen of Narnia desires a safe conduct to come and speak with you.

MR. BEAVER. Queen of Narnia indeed! Of all the cheek—

ASLAN. Peace, Beaver. *(To the DWARF.)* Tell your mistress that I grant her safe conduct on condition that she leaves her wand behind at that great oak. That way she can play no magical trick.

DWARF *(sneering, under his breath)*. The magic she plans requires no trick. *(He exits.)*

3RD ANIMAL. What can she possibly want here?

4TH ANIMAL. She's up to no good, I can tell you.

5TH ANIMAL *(shivering)*. Brrr! I can feel the chill of her presence already.

6TH ANIMAL. Shh—there she is.

(The WITCH and DWARF enter.)

WITCH. You have a traitor there, Aslan!

ASLAN. His offense was not against you.

WITCH. Have you forgotten the Deep Magic?

ASLAN. Tell me of it.

WITCH. Tell you? Tell you what is written on that very table of stone which stands beside us? You know the magic which the Emperor put into Narnia at the beginning of time. You know that every traitor belongs to me—and that for every treachery, I have a right to kill. *(A pause as ALL react in fear.)*

ALL *(quietly)*. Oh, no. Can it be true? Is it really written? *(Etc.)*

WITCH *(pointing to EDMUND)*. And so, that human creature is mine. His life is forfeit to me. His blood is my property. *(She laughs haughtily. PETER withdraws his sword and stands as a shield in front of EDMUND.)*

PETER. Come and take him then.

ASLAN. Peace!

WITCH *(to PETER)*. Fool! Do you think you can rob me of my rights by mere force? *(Indicating ASLAN.)* Your master knows what is written. *He* knows that unless the Law is obeyed, all Narnia will be overturned and perish in fire and water. *(A pause as ALL look toward ASLAN.)*

ASLAN. It is true. I do not deny it. *(ALL voice grave concern.)*

ALL. Oh, no. This is terrible. What is to be done? Will she take the boy? *(Etc.)*

SUSAN. Oh, Aslan. Can't we do something about the Deep Magic? Isn't there something you can work against it?

ASLAN. Not against the Emperor's magic. *(A pause.)* But I *will* talk to the witch.

DWARF. You mean the *Queen.*

2ND ANIMAL. Shut up, you toad!

ASLAN. Peace — Peace! Fall back, all of you. *(ALL except ASLAN and the WITCH move to the side. The DWARF stands near the WITCH who converses in a low voice with ASLAN.)*

LUCY. Oh, Edmund.

SUSAN. Why did we ever leave that wardrobe?

EDMUND. I wish we could go back.

PETER. So do I. But I'm not sure we could find the way. At any rate, we're needed here — now more than ever.

1ST ANIMAL. This suspense is awful.

2ND ANIMAL. What are they talking about?

3RD ANIMAL. Do you think He can save the boy?

MRS. BEAVER. If anything can possibly be done, Aslan will think of it. *(ASLAN and the WITCH nod in agreement and end their conversation.)*

ASLAN *(to the OTHERS)*. The matter has been settled. The witch has renounced the claim on your brother's blood. Edmund is free. *(ALL are deeply relieved as they cheer softly.)*

WITCH *(triumphantly to the DWARF)*. Now gather our forces. The time is at hand. *(To ASLAN.)* One final thing. How do I know your promise will be kept?

ASLAN *(sternly)*. You know that when Aslan makes a promise, *it will be kept. (He roars loudly as the WITCH and DWARF exit quickly.)*

SUSAN. Aslan, what did she mean? What promise did you make to her?

ASLAN. Do not be concerned for that. Now, all of you must move away from here at once. This place will be needed for another purpose. Go to the Fields of Beruna. There you shall camp tonight.

PETER. Are you not going with us?

ASLAN. I am needed here. *(Putting his arm around PETER.)* Peter, the witch has business in these parts. When she has finished, you and the others must be prepared for anything—perhaps even a battle of life or death.

PETER. But you will be here to help us, won't you, Aslan?

ASLAN. I can give no promise of that. Now go, everyone. You must get a good night's rest to be ready for whatever tomorrow may bring. Please, go at once.

(Worried and anxious, ALL obey and exit. When they are gone, ASLAN begins to pace slowly to and fro. He appears drained of strength and energy. Quietly and cautiously, LUCY and SUSAN re-enter, watching

ASLAN intently. He becomes aware of their presence. They try to hide.)

ASLAN. Children—children. Why did you not go with the others?

LUCY. We're very worried, Aslan.

SUSAN. We're sure something dreadful is going to happen.

LUCY. May we stay with you, Aslan?

SUSAN. Please?

ASLAN *(after a pause).* Yes...yes. I will be happy to have your company for a few moments. But when I tell you to leave, you must.

LUCY. Oh, we will.

SUSAN. Thank you. Thank you. *(He turns from them and drops to his knees wearily.)*

LUCY. Aslan! Dear Aslan, what is wrong?

SUSAN. Are you ill, dear Aslan?

ASLAN. No. I am sad and lonely. Lay your hands on my mane so that I can feel you close to me. *(LUCY and SUSAN kneel with ASLAN and stroke his mane. After a few moments, he rises.)* Now, children, you must leave me alone at this time. If you wish to stay nearby, you may. But you must hide.

LUCY. But, Aslan—

ASLAN. Under no circumstances can you let yourselves be seen. *(Loud, strange noises are heard offstage.)*

SUSAN *(alarmed).* What is that?

VOICES *(off).* Here is the place! Do you see him? We will end his visit here! He is ours! *(Etc.)*

ASLAN. Farewell, my children. Leave this instant.

LUCY. But we're afraid you'll—

ASLAN. Hide quickly. Now!

(LUCY and SUSAN hide as the WITCH, her ARMY and the DWARF enter.)

WITCH. The fool is here! Bind him fast. *(Several ARMY MEMBERS tie Aslan's hands and feet.)* Let him be shaved! *(Two or three ARMY MEMBERS withdraw large shears and cut off Aslan's mane. LUCY and SUSAN, unseen by the others react in horror.)*

1ST ARMY MEMBER. Look. Why, he's only a great big cat, after all.

2ND ARMY MEMBER. Is *that* what we were afraid of? *(ALL laugh and taunt ASLAN.)*

ALL. Pussy-cat, pussy-cat. Hello, stupid pussy-cat. How many mice have you caught today? Would you like a saucer of milk? *(Etc.)*

LUCY *(whispering to SUSAN)*. How can they?

SUSAN *(whispering)*. The brutes.

WITCH. Muzzle him! *(Two ARMY MEMBERS strap a muzzle around Aslan's mouth. ALL give a low, menacing laugh.)*

LUCY *(whispering)*. Why doesn't he bite off their hands?

SUSAN *(whispering)*. He would never betray the Deep Magic.

LUCY *(whispering)*. The cowards. They know he could kill them all — but he will not. *(The ARMY MEMBERS laugh and cheer as ASLAN is muzzled.)*

WITCH. Now place him on the altar. *(Several ARMY MEMBERS roughly push ASLAN prone onto the Stone Table.)* Sentinels — erect our banner here at the site of our victory.

(Two SENTINELS bring on a large banner attached to two large standards. The banner bears the crest of the

witch. It is stretched out in front of the Stone Table and set in place by sliding the standards into sleeves at the front corners of the table (or the standards may be free-standing) so that ASLAN is completely hidden from the view of the audience. The WITCH stands on the table behind the banner. Only her head and arms are visible. The ARMY MEMBERS gather around the table.)

WITCH. Now who has won, you fool? Did you think by sacrificing yourself you would save the human traitor? Not only will I kill you in his place as we agreed, but I will come back and kill the boy as well. In that knowledge, despair and die! *(Unseen behind the banner, she stabs ASLAN who is heard to groan. LUCY and SUSAN cover their eyes in grief. The WITCH reappears from behind the banner.)* Aslan is mine! Victory is mine! Narnia is mine! *(The ARMY MEMBERS cheer and laugh maniacally.)* Now follow me, and we will set about finishing what remains of this war. It will not take us long to crush the human vermin and the young traitor, now that the great fool—the great cat—lies dead. *(ALL cheer as they exit. A moment later, LUCY and SUSAN emerge from their hiding place and move cautiously toward the Stone Table which is still hidden by the banner. They go to the head of the table—standing clear of the banner—and look down at the body of the unseen ASLAN.)*

SUSAN. How horrible. How unfair. Nothing seems to matter now.

LUCY. I can't bear the look of that horrible muzzle. *(She reaches behind the banner.)* I wonder if I can take it off. *(She struggles, then withdraws the muzzle from behind the banner.)*

SUSAN. Good work, Lu. I wonder if we can untie him as
    well. *(They struggle with the unseen ropes.)* It's no use.
    The ropes are much too tight.

LUCY *(jumping back)*. Look!

SUSAN. Ugh! What's that?

LUCY. They look like mice.

SUSAN. Go away! Go away you little beasts.

LUCY. Wait! Can you see what they're doing?

SUSAN *(after a pause, looking closer)*. They're nibbling
    away at the ropes.

LUCY. I think they're friendly mice. Poor little things—
    they don't realize he's dead. They think it'll do some
    good untying him. But, of course, it won't. *(Thunder is
    heard as lightning flashes.)* What's that?

SUSAN. Maybe it's the witch and her evil army again.
    Perhaps they've killed the others and are coming back
    for us. *(Louder thunder and brighter lightning fill the sky.
    LUCY and SUSAN rush to their hiding place. After a
    few moments, the thunder and lightning subside. LUCY
    and SUSAN come out of hiding.)*

LUCY. It was only a storm.

SUSAN. It didn't last long, but it was very strong. I think
    the lightning must have hit something around here. I
    heard a terrible crack.

LUCY. I wish it had hit this horrible banner. I'm going to
    tear it down.

SUSAN. No, Lu. What if the witch comes back and sees
    you?

LUCY. I don't care. She plans to kill us all anyway. *(She
    grabs at the banner.)*

SUSAN. That's true. Here, let me help you. *(Angrily, they
    tear at the banner, pulling up the standards and over-
    turning them. The Stone Table is revealed to be cracked*

into two pieces. ASLAN is gone. LUCY and SUSAN stare in disbelief. SUSAN is in tears.) He's gone.

LUCY. Oh, no. They might at least have left the body alone.

SUSAN. Has the witch done this, too? What does it mean? Is it more magic?

(ASLAN enters U bathed in a pool of bright light. He appears stronger than before, and his mane is fully grown again.)

ASLAN. Yes! It *is* more magic. *(LUCY and SUSAN are awe-struck.)*

LUCY. Oh, Aslan!

SUSAN. Are you not dead, dear Aslan?

ASLAN. Not now.

LUCY. You're not a gho—ghos—?

ASLAN. Do I look like one? *(LUCY and SUSAN rush to him, laughing and crying simultaneously. They embrace ASLAN.)*

LUCY. Oh, you're real, you're real! Oh, Aslan. *(After a few moments they calm down.)*

SUSAN. But what does it all mean?

ASLAN. It means there is an even Deeper Magic than the witch knew. Before time began, there was another law written. It says that when a willing victim who has committed no treachery—

LUCY. Like you?

ASLAN. Like me—is killed in the place of a traitor—

SUSAN. Like Edmund?

ASLAN. Like Edmund. The table will crack, and Death itself will start working backward.

LUCY and SUSAN. Like now! *(ALL embrace again.)*

ASLAN. Oh, children, I feel my strength coming back. I feel that I am going to roar a very loud roar. You'd better put your fingers in your ears. *(LUCY and SUSAN cover their ears as ASLAN emits an earth-shattering roar.)* Now the time has come for our last battle against the witch and her evil forces.

SUSAN. We must hurry, Aslan. The witch and her army are looking for the others at this very minute.

ASLAN. Then we shall add more soldiers to our own army.

LUCY. Who else will join us?

ASLAN. Those who await us at the witch's castle.

SUSAN. What are they doing there?

ASLAN. Nothing. At the moment they are only stone statues, but I shall breathe the breath of life into them, and they will be made whole again.

LUCY. Do you suppose Mr. Tumnus is there?

ASLAN. Was he an enemy of the witch?

LUCY. Yes—because of me.

ASLAN. Then I am certain he is there.

LUCY. Oh, I can't wait to see Mr. Tumnus again.

ASLAN. And you shall, Lucy, my dear, you shall. Now take hold of my mane, both of you. We will fly to the home of the witch and rescue our awaiting allies. Away! Away!

(They exit quickly. A moment later, the WOOD NYMPHS enter and remove the Stone Table, the banner and standards. After they exit, PETER and EDMUND enter. Both are tired and weary.)

EDMUND. The storm woke me in the night, Peter.

PETER. It woke me as well. And I couldn't fall back to sleep.

EDMUND. By the way, did you see the girls this morning?

PETER. No—nor did I see Aslan. I'm worried about them. Where could they be?

(MR. and MRS. BEAVER enter.)

MRS. BEAVER. Good morning, Peter...Edmund.

PETER. Hello.

EDMUND. Good morning, Mr. and Mrs. Beaver.

MR. BEAVER. The others are stirring, but no one seems to know quite what to do next.

(The UNICORN, CENTAUR and ANIMALS enter slowly.)

MRS. BEAVER. We need to find Aslan—to ask him for guidance. *(Suddenly a loud, fearsome noise is heard offstage.)*

1ST ANIMAL. What is that?

2ND ANIMAL. If it is the witch and her army, it could be the end for us.

3RD ANIMAL. Without Aslan, we are lost.

EDMUND. But we shall not go down without a fight.

PETER. Yes. Edmund is right. *(To EDMUND, handing him a dagger.)* Take this dagger. Lucy left it in my care. *(To the OTHERS.)* If this indeed is to be our last day, let it be marked with valor and honor!

(ALL agree. Suddenly, the WITCH and her ARMY enter. They wield swords and knives. A fierce fight begins.

The WITCH touches three or four ANIMALS with her wand and they become "frozen" statues. When ED-MUND sees this, he rushes toward the WITCH and knocks the wand from her hand with his dagger. He picks the wand up, breaks it and tosses it away. The WITCH draws her dagger and advances toward PETER. The Witch's ARMY is getting the better of the out-numbered, mostly unarmed ANIMALS. PETER and the WITCH begin to fight. Her ARMY surrounds EDMUND as most of the ANIMALS lie wounded or stand "frozen." Suddenly, triumphant offstage noises are heard. ASLAN enters swiftly, leading his FOLLOWERS, along with LUCY and SUSAN. The wounded ANIMALS cheer the arrival. ASLAN quickly goes to the "frozen" ANIMALS and blows on them gently. They come "back to life" and re-join the fighting. The Witch's ARMY begins to retreat. The WITCH knocks the sword from Peter's hand and advances on him with her knife. ASLAN suddenly lunges at the WITCH. They roll on the ground until finally the WITCH lies motionless, apparently slain by her own knife. ALL have been watching and are stunned into silence for a moment.)

MEMBERS of the WITCH'S ARMY. She's dead! Our Queen's dead! The battle is lost! Retreat! Retreat! *(Etc. The Witch's ARMY, now battered and bruised, screams and begins to flee. Two or three of them drag the WITCH off as the ANIMALS, PETER, EDMUND, SUSAN and LUCY cheer.)*

PETER and EDMUND. Victory!

PETER, EDMUND, SUSAN and LUCY. Victory!

ALL. Victory! *(Except for the few who lie wounded, ALL embrace and congratulate each other, then surround ASLAN.)*

ASLAN. Lucy, minister to the wounded.

LUCY. But what can I do?

ASLAN. Have you forgotten your gift? *(A brief pause as she takes out the bottle.)*

LUCY. Oh, yes. The cordial that Father Christmas gave to me. He said a few drops would help restore one to health. *(She hands the bottle to the WOUNDED who drink and are revived.)*

ASLAN. We welcome the new members of our army— those who have so long been under the curse of the witch. *(ALL shake hands with the NEWCOMERS and welcome them.)*

LUCY. I was so hoping to see Mr. Tumnus among you.

1ST NEWCOMER. I thought I saw Aslan bring him back to life.

2ND NEWCOMER. As did I.

LUCY. But, alas, he is not here. I fear I shall never see him again.

ASLAN. Peter, you are to be commended. You fought well against the witch until we arrived.

PETER. Edmund's the real hero. If he hadn't destroyed the witch's magic wand, she'd have turned us all to stone.

EDMUND. It was the least I could do—after the wrong I've done.

ASLAN *(putting his arm around EDMUND)*. All have done wrong, Edmund—at one time or another. But to acknowledge your error and try to do better is the best way to right that wrong. And that is what you have done. *(He shakes hands with EDMUND.)*

PETER. Aslan, what will happen to the witch's army? Are we still in danger of them?

ASLAN. They will have little power now that their leader is dead. But they will always be about—lurking in forbidden corners. So you must be aware of them. always be on guard.

ALL. Yes, Aslan.

ASLAN. And now, the only duty remaining from our victory is to crown the new rulers of Narnia. *(ALL cheer and applaud.)* I wish that I could crown them on this very spot at this very moment. But we shall have to wait until we reach Cair Paravel. That is where the four crowns are.

(TUMNUS enters out of breath, carrying an ornately decorated wooden box.)

TUMNUS. No they're not, Lord Aslan. They are here. *(He produces four crowns from the box. ALL cheer.)*

LUCY. Mr. Tumnus! *(She embraces TUMNUS.)*

TUMNUS *(to ASLAN)*. After you freed me at the witch's castle, I ran to Cair Paravel—as fast as my hooves would carry me—so that I could get the crowns. I suspected they would be needed here.

UNICORN. I suspect you just wanted to avoid the battle with the witch.

TUMNUS. What good would a faun be in a fight? I'm known as Tumnus the Trembler, not Tumnus the Terrible. *(ALL laugh.)*

ASLAN. Thank you, Tumnus, for your thoughtfulness, whatever the motive. And now, let the coronation begin. *(He motions for PETER, SUSAN, EDMUND and LUCY to kneel. He takes a crown from the box which*

TUMNUS holds. He will repeat the action for each crowning.) King Peter. *(He places a crown on Peter's head.)*

ALL *(repeating solemnly).* King Peter.

ASLAN *(crowning SUSAN).* Queen Susan.

ALL. Queen Susan.

ASLAN *(crowning EDMUND).* King Edmund.

ALL. King Edmund.

ASLAN *(crowning LUCY).* Queen Lucy.

ALL. Queen Lucy. *(ASLAN motions for them to rise.)* Long live the Kings and Queens of Narnia! *(ALL cheer.)*

ASLAN. And now, you shall all repair to Cair Paravel where the rulers will ascend their thrones, and the coronation celebration will begin. *(ALL cheer and begin to leave. ASLAN stays behind.)*

CENTAUR. Aslan—will you not be there, too?

ASLAN. Momentarily. For a little while at least. Now join the others, and go in peace. Cair Paravel has been dark and empty for much too long. *(The CENTAUR joins the OTHERS as they exit chanting, "Long live King Peter! Long live Queen Susan! Long live King Edmund! Long live Queen Lucy!" Their voices fade in the distance. ASLAN is now alone.)* Yes, I will join them shortly, but I cannot stay with them long—for I have many other jobs to do, beginning with one right here. *(He claps his hands twice.)* Wood Nymphs! Please return the lamppost to its rightful place here in the forest.

(Two WOOD NYMPHS enter and set the lamppost where it originally was, then exit. ASLAN crosses to the lamppost.)

ASLAN. The children will rule for a long while, but the day will come when they need to return from whence they came. The lamppost shall be their guide.

(He exits. Pipe music is heard offstage. A moment later, TUMNUS, playing his pipe, and MR. and MRS. BEAVER enter.)

MRS. BEAVER. You played so very nicely at Cair Paravel, Mr. Tumnus. You enchanted us all.

—TUMNUS. Thank you, Mrs. Beaver. But I'm afraid I *Stage Centa* stayed there much too long.

MR. BEAVER. As did we all.

MRS. BEAVER. But it was so hard to leave. The feasting—the dancing—the music. Day after day. Month after month.

TUMNUS. And with such good rulers leading us, too.

MRS. BEAVER. They've certainly earned their new names.

TUMNUS. King Peter the Magnificent.

MRS. BEAVER. Queen Susan the Gentle.

MR. BEAVER. King Edmund the Just.

MRS. BEAVER. Queen Lucy the Valiant.

—TUMNUS. You know, it occurred to me—no one has seen Aslan now for quite a while.

MRS. BEAVER. Oh, he comes and goes. One day you'll see him—another you won't.

MR. BEAVER. And, of course, he has other countries to attend to.

MRS. BEAVER. Other duties. Just as we all do. Well, goodbye, Mr. Tumnus. I have chores to do.

MR. BEAVER. And I have dams to build.

— TUMNUS. And I have tunes to play. Goodbye.

(TUMNUS begins to play his pipe as they exit in opposite directions. A moment later, the WHITE STAG enters, pauses briefly, then exits quickly.)

Stage left

EDMUND'S VOICE *(off)*. I saw the White Stag here, fair sisters and good brother.
SUSAN'S VOICE *(off)*. As did I.
LUCY'S VOICE *(off)*. And I.

(EDMUND, SUSAN, LUCY and PETER enter. They wear robes as well as crowns.)

PETER. I've never pursued a nobler quarry. Where did he go?
SUSAN *(pointing)*. Into that thicket, I believe.
EDMUND. A very dense thicket—filled with briars and underbrush.
PETER. But we shall not turn back. As kings and queens, we always achieve what we set out to accomplish.
LUCY. Our brother is right.
SUSAN. Before we pursue the White Stag further, I suggest we remove our robes and crowns so they will not become torn or damaged in yon thicket.
PETER. Yes. We shall leave them here until we return. *(They begin to take off their robes and crowns. ED-MUND moves slightly to the right of the lamppost.)*
EDMUND. This lamp on the post worketh strangely upon me—as though I have seen it before—in a dream.
LUCY *(joining EDMUND at the right of the lamppost)*. I feel the same. It seemeth to me that a strange adventure lies on this side of the lamppost.
EDMUND *(as he and LUCY place their robes and crowns carefully on the ground next to the lamppost)*. Well

then—in the name of Aslan, let us go and take the adventure that shall fall to us! *(He and LUCY exit quickly off, R.)*

PETER. Wait for us, good brother and sister! *(He and SUSAN finish taking off their robes and crowns and set them next to those of LUCY and EDMUND, crossing to the right of the lamppost as they do so.)*

SUSAN. Brother...this lamppost worketh strangely upon me just as it did with Lucy and Edmund.

PETER. I, too, feel its peculiar effect.

LUCY'S VOICE *(off)*. Hey, where are we?

PETER *(calling off, R)*. You're in the thicket, of course.

EDMUND'S VOICE *(off)*. No—we're not! We're in—in a wardrobe!

SUSAN. Wardrobe?

PETER *(a slight recognition, almost to himself)*. The wardrobe. I'd forgotten all about it.

SUSAN *(also remembering)*. Yes...me, too.

LUCY'S VOICE *(off)*. The room hasn't changed at all. And the clock has hardly moved.

EDMUND'S VOICE *(off)*. Hurry, you two! Perhaps we'll still be in time for dinner!

SUSAN *(wistfully)*. It—it must be time to leave, Peter.

PETER. I suppose it is.

SUSAN. Peter, do you think we'll ever find our way back to Narnia again?

PETER. If we're lucky, Susan. If we're very, very lucky.

(They take a fond last look at Narnia, then exit. As they are leaving, ASLAN enters, unseen by them, and looks at them affectionately as they go. He then turns to the AUDIENCE.)

ASLAN. Yes, the children *will* find their way back here again. Perhaps not through the wardrobe—but there are other paths that lead to Narnia. Oh yes, they will return someday. For once a King in Narnia—always a King. Once a Queen—always a Queen. It is important that they return, for good people need good rulers. And good rulers need good people. That, perhaps, is the Deepest Magic of all.

(He exits as the general lights fade, leaving a special light on the crowns and robes. A moment later, all lights fade to blackout.)

THE END

ABOUT THE AUTHORS

C. S. LEWIS (1898-1963) was the author of forty books which include novels, histories, essays and poetry. He was educated at University College, Oxford, England, where he was an outstanding scholar. He went on to become professor of medieval and Renaissance English at Cambridge University.

Among Lewis' works are "The Screwtape Letters," "Allegory of Love" and "Surprised by Joy." Perhaps his best-known writings are the "Chronicles of Narnia," seven fairy tales which include "The Lion, the Witch and the Wardrobe" (1950), one of the world's most widely acclaimed children's classics.

Joseph Robinette is the author of twenty-one published plays and musicals, two of which—"The Fabulous Fable Factory," written with composer Thomas Tierney, and "Charlotte's Web," dramatized from E. B. White—are among the most widely produced children's plays in the United States. He has also dramatized the authorized stage versions of "Anne of Green Gables," "The Paper Chase" and "A Rose for Emily."

Recipient of numerous playwriting honors, Robinette was awarded the 1976 Charlotte Chorpenning Cup, presented annually by the Children's Theatre Association of America to "an outstanding writer of children's plays who has achieved national recognition." Robinette currently resides in New Jersey where he is Professor of Speech and Theatre at Glassboro State College.

DIRECTOR'S NOTES

DIRECTOR'S NOTES

DIRECTOR'S NOTES